EIGHT
LITTLE INDIANS

By Josephine Lovell

Copyright 1935 and 1936
By
The Platt & Munk Co., Inc.
Made in U. S. A.

·NEW·YORK·
THE·PLATT·&·MUNK·CO INC·

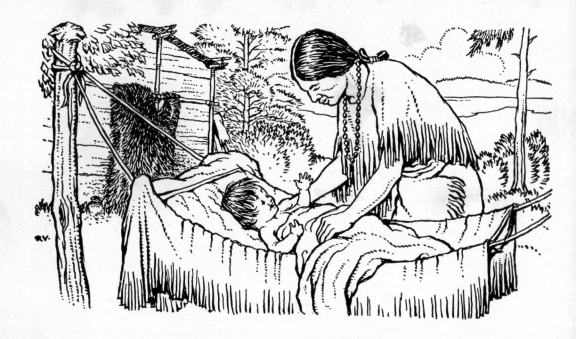

LEAPING TROUT—A LITTLE IROQUOIS BOY

Leaping Trout was two years old before he had any name except "Baby." Almost every day his grandmother said to his mother: "Why don't you give the baby a name?" And every time his mother answered; "I can't think of any name that suits him."

When he was two years old, his father, Swift Panther, said it was time he learned to swim. The Iroquois Indians loved the water. They were great swimmers and swift paddlers in their birchbark canoes.

So, hand in hand, Baby and his father went down to the shore of the lake. Baby loved the water. He had often played around in it. But he had never before been in water deeper than his waist.

At first Swift Panther kept his hand under his son's chest. But Baby paddled with his hands and kicked out his feet, just as his father did. Soon he was swimming along alone, just like a little puppy.

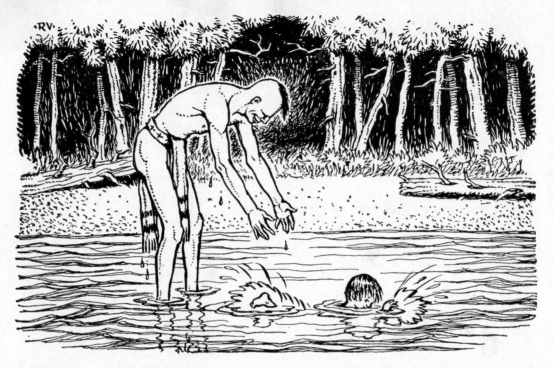

After they had been swimming for quite a long time,
Swift Panther said they must go back to the shore. When
they reached shallow water, Swift Panther stood up. But
Baby swam on, until his knees hit the sand on the bottom
of the lake.

"That's as far as you can swim," said his father. "Stand
up, now. We must go home."

Baby rolled over on his back and laughed.

"No! No!" he said. "I like the water. I don't want to go
home."

Swift Panther reached down to pick him up. But Baby
squirmed around and curved his body, as a fish does
in shallow water and slipped away from him. His father
laughed.

"Come little leaping trout," he said, as he picked Baby up and set him on his shoulder. "You shall be called Leaping Trout, until you are a man and win a warrior's name by some brave deed."

When Leaping Trout was seven, his father let him help in the making of a birchbark canoe. First they made a frame of willow branches. Then Swift Panther picked out a large white birch tree, with perfect bark. He cut around the bark close to the ground. Then he made a second cut near to the lowest branches. After this, he cut straight down between these circles. Then he lifted one edge and pulled the bark from the tree, in one piece. This made the body of the canoe.

Leaping Trout helped his father stretch the bark over

the willow frame. They sewed up the ends with strips of willow bark. Then they spread the sap of the spruce tree, over the seams. When this dried, not a drop of water could get through.

When the canoe was finished, Swift Panther picked it up and laid it lightly on the water.

"Step into the canoe, my son," he said. "It is yours. You have often paddled with me. Now you may paddle alone.

I know that you will be safe. Even if you should over-
turn your canoe, you will be in no danger of drowning.
One who swims like a fish is as safe as a fish, in water."

Leaping Trout could hardly believe that the beautiful
canoe was really his. But at his father's words, he lifted
the paddle above his head. That was his way of saying
"Thank you."

Soon he was paddling out over the lake. All morning
he kept on. He would have liked to stay in the canoe all
day. But when the sun stood straight above his head, he
knew that it was dinner time. He was hungry, so he
turned the bow of the canoe toward home and paddled as
fast as he could.

Every day through the summer and autumn, he went off in his canoe. Sometimes he took some food and stayed all day. Soon he knew the lake, almost as well as Swift Panther himself did. But, though he loved his canoe and became the swiftest paddler in the tribe, he always liked swimming better than anything else.

Swift Panther was chief of his band. Leaping Trout would some day be chief. When he was ten years old, his father decided to have a feast and ask all his friends to it. He sent a messenger through the woods to give the invitations. To prove that the messenger was really from him, he sent along his best wampum bead belt.

Wampum was made from shells. Most of it was white,

because it was made from white snail shells, or the pearly part of clam shells. But Iroquois Indians cut purple beads from the dark part of the clam shell. This was hard to cut and polish. So it was more valuable than white.

Because Swift Panther was a chief, his belt had many rows of purple wampum. His friends knew that it was his belt. When the messenger showed it, they knew the invitation really came from their chief. Otherwise they might have thought it was a trick of some enemy, to lead them into danger.

The day of the feast, the Indians who were invited came from far and near and smoked the pipe of friendship with Swift Panther. There was a great feast. Leaping Trout and the other boys had a wonderful time, with games and races, on land and on the lake. When the fun was over everyone agreed that it was the best time they ever had.

LEAPING TROUT

Have you ever been out paddling
In a really true canoe?

See! Leaping Trout just loves it
And he helped to make it too.

His father taught him how to swim
When he was hardly grown.

So now he paddles everywhere
And does it all alone.

WINONA.   A Little Indian of the Prairies

Winona was the daughter of a chief.   Her father, Great Thunder, was a leader among the Sioux.   He was a rich man because he owned many horses.   He was also a brave hunter.

Great Thunder's teepee was large.   It was made of poles woven together at the top.   Over the poles Winona's mother spread buffalo skins, which she had sewn together. On the skins, Great Thunder had painted pictures of his brave deeds.

All summer the tribe moved about over the prairies, looking for buffalo and deer. They had no gardens. Winona had meat for most of her meals.   She liked it and the good broth her mother made from it.

Sometimes she had wild fruit.   Her mother dried some of

the wild berries and mixed them with dried meat. This was
called pemmican. It made good food for the winter, when
fresh meat was hard to get.

Winona loved to travel over the prairies, best of all when

her father took her on his horse. The horse was called
Painted Pony. He had brown and white spots. A horse
of this kind is sometimes called a piebald horse and sometimes a pinto pony.

Great Thunder did not use a saddle. He rode bareback.
When he wanted Painted Pony to run very fast, he touched
him on the neck or whispered into his ear. Then the horse
went like the wind. He seemed to know as much as a hu-
man being. Winona loved to ride on his back.

All summer Painted Pony ate the long grass of the prairie.
When fall came, Great Thunder stripped the bark from
trees to make winter food for his horses. Winona liked to
feed Painted Pony. She gave him cottonwood bark for his
regular meals. Sometimes as a treat she gave him strips of
poplar bark. He liked that very much and it kept him well
and strong during the winter.

One morning when Winona awoke, she heard the wind whistling around the teepee.

"Whee—"Whee-ee-sh!" it screamed.

Winona sat up. She had no bed except a buffalo skin. In warm weather she spread the skin on the ground, with the furry side down, and slept on it. When the weather turned cold, she laid it with the furry side up. Then she rolled herself up in it. She was really "as snug as a bug in a rug."

This windy morning, her mother was taking down bags from the poles of the teepee.

"Wazeah, the God of Storms, is screaming outside," she said. "We must make ready for winter for it will soon be here."

During the summer, Winona's mother built her fire outside of the teepee. This morning she had made it inside.
It was in the center of the teepee. Above it was a hole
in the top. This was to let the smoke out. Winona ran

over and sat beside the fire, while she ate her breakfast.

Mother began to dress Winona's baby brother. He had not been given a name yet. Everyone called him Papoose. That is the Indian word for baby.

Mother laid a buffalo skin on the ground. On this she spread a soft white doeskin. Then from a bag she took handfuls of cattail fluff. It was as soft and white as swansdown. She spread this over the doeskin. She laid her baby down on it. Then she rolled him up, so that only his little face showed.

Winona laughed. He looked so cunning as he smiled and tried to talk.

"He looks just like a big cocoon, with a baby's face at the top," she said. Mother smiled. Then she wrapped a dark, furry covering around the white doeskin and put Papoose into his carrying case. This was also his cradle. She hung the case up on a pole of the teepee. Papoose looked like a doll in a white girl's Christmas stocking.

"He is safe from Wazeah now," said Mother.

Winona helped unpack the winter clothes for the rest of the family. There were warm moccasins and leggings and shirts for everyone. For Father there were some extra

large moccasins. They were made of buffalo skin with the fur inside.

Just then Great Thunder came into the teepee. He was very tall and handsome. He wore long leggings of deer-skin with fringe down the sides. They came up almost to his waist and were tied to his belt. His chest and arms were bare.

His head was shaved, except for one long lock of hair on top. This was his scalp lock. Winona knew that when he went to war, he fought bravely to keep the enemy from getting this lock. Around his head, he wore a broad band of leather, decorated with porcupine quills. He had a great bonnet of eagle feathers, to wear when he went on the warpath. But now the Indians were at peace, so the war bonnet hung in the teepee.

"I see you are getting out the winter garments," he said.
"It is well."

He took off his moccasins and lined them with some
loose buffalo hair. Indians did not wear socks, but when

he put the moccasins on again, the hair inside felt like warm woollen stockings. Over the moccasins he pulled the great, fur-lined pair his wife had just unpacked.

"Why do you put on the fur moccasins?" asked Mother. "It is not yet very cold."

"No," Father replied, "but soon we shall have snow. The food scouts report buffalo three days' ride away, and we are going now to hunt. It will be very cold before we come home."

"It is good that the buffalo are near," said Mother. "We have some dried meat and some pemmican, but not enough for the whole winter. If you bring back meat from the hunt, we need not fear Eyah."

Winona knew that Eyah was the God of Famine. Grandmother had told her stories about him. One winter, when Grandmother was a little girl, Eyah had come to the teepees of her tribe, and everyone had been very hungry. Winona was glad that the buffalo had been found, by the food scouts. She knew that when Great Thunder and his hunters came back, they would bring plenty of meat, for all the teepees of the tribe.

WINONA

Winona is this Prairie maid
Oh, you should see her ride!

She sits her Pinto pony well
And always rides astride.

She follows deer and buffalo
Across the bare Prairie

Then sleeps at night so snug and warm
Within her own teepee.

GRAY BIRD—A LITTLE PLAINS INDIAN

Gray Bird was a little Indian boy. He lived on the great plains. During the winter, the chief of his tribe picked out a sheltered spot at the edge of the forest for their home. When spring came they packed up and started for the hunting grounds.

Gray Bird's father was named Big Wolf, because he was so strong and tall and brave. His mother was White Swan. He had an older brother, Running Deer, and a younger sister, Little Fawn. They all lived together in a tent with a pointed top. It was called a teepee.

When Big Wolf's chief decided that it was time to move,

MCMXXXV by THE PLATT & MUNK CO., Inc.

Big Wolf and his family did not leave their home behind them as white men do when they move. Gray Bird's mother took the teepee down and rolled it up and tied it on a travois behind a horse.

Then wherever they stopped, she put it up and that was their home.

To make a travois White Swan tied two poles to a horse. She fastened one on each side, with the other end dragging on the ground behind the horse. Then she put the teepee and the bundles of clothing and food and dishes across the two poles and tied them on tight. When everything was ready, she climbed up on the horse's back and rode off with the ends of the travois dragging behind her. Nearly everything was carried in this way.

Big Wolf did not help White Swan take down or put up the teepee. He was a hunter and a warrior and was not expected to do any of the work around the camp. Little boys like Gray Bird helped their mothers. When they grew

as big as Running Deer they rode with the men and no one thought of asking them to help do any of the women's work.

Sometimes White Swan took Little Fawn up on the horse with her. Sometimes, especially when Little Fawn was sleepy, she packed her in with the soft bundles on the travois. When Little Fawn was a tiny baby she traveled on her mother's back, in a papoose case. An Indian baby is called a papoose.

When Gray Bird was a papoose he was carried in a papoose case, too, but as soon as he could walk his mother let him run about with her while she worked. By the time he was six years old, he could beat many of the big boys of nine and ten at running.

Gray Bird's grandfather and grandmother taught him a great many interesting things. When he was only three, his grandfather began to teach him about the birds and animals of the forest. He also taught him to imitate the sounds

they made. He taught him to be quiet and patient and to step lightly and never to kill animals or birds needlessly. When he was five Gray Bird could move so silently through the forest trails, that he could come almost within arm's

reach of a squirrel, before little fuzzy tail ran chattering up a tree.

Once when he was running silently down a trail in the woods, he almost bumped into a bear cub. The little bear was quite as surprised as Gray Bird was. They stood and looked at each other for a moment. Gray Bird would have liked to make friends with the little bear, but his grandfather had told him never to do such a thing when alone.

"A little cub is harmless," Grandfather said, "but where there is a cub, there is a mother bear not far away. If you tried to make friends with the cub, the mother might think you were going to hurt her baby. So be sure to leave bear cubs alone, until you are older and have won the right to be a hunter."

Gray Bird remembered Grandfather's warning now. Instead of going toward the friendly looking little cub, he backed quietly away and hid behind some bushes at the side of the trail. He was glad he had obeyed, when he saw a great mother bear running clumsily down the trail toward the cub.

The old bear licked the head of the little one. Then she gave it a cuff and sent it off down the trail, away from Gray Bird. When they were out of sight, the boy stepped back onto the trail and ran home as fast as he could.

Gray Bird had a dog named Bushy. Sometimes he made a travois by fastening two strips of wood to Bushy as White Swan did by fastening the poles to a horse. Then he stretched a blanket between the strips and took a ride be-

hind his dog. Bushy didn't like to be used as a horse, and when he saw Gray Bird coming toward him with the harness, he would run into the woods or hide behind the teepee.

The best time to catch him was when he was eating, so

when Gray Bird wanted to take a ride, he would ask his mother for a bone with a little meat on it. When Bushy had a bone to pick he was so interested in it he would not even notice Gray Bird, and before he knew it he would be harnessed up.

After his ride Gray Bird usually gave Bushy another bone, as a reward. Then Bushy was happy. He would gnaw and growl, and gnaw and growl. But Gray Bird did not mind the growling. He knew that was Bushy's way of showing his pleasure in the bone.

GRAY BIRD

This little Indian loves his dog
As all small children do.

They play together every day
We know they're happy too.

"Jump for the bone" says "Gray Bird"
It's just above your head.

The doggie looked and looked at it
"Bow wow" is what he said.

ANTELOPE—A NAVAHO INDIAN BOY

Antelope was a Navaho Indian. The house in which he lived was made of poles, covered with earth and grass. Such a house is called a hogan. All around the hogan were miles of sand. Only sage bushes and coarse grass grew on the sand.

Every morning, Antelope drove his mother's flock of sheep and goats out of their pen. All day he wandered around with them, looking for the places where the grass grew thickest.

While he was taking care of the flock, his mother, White Cloud, sat outside the hogan door. She was weaving a blanket. She made it of wool clipped from her own sheep.

Not far away, beside a small fire, Antelope's father, Red Eagle, was hammering silver. He was making jewelry. Sometimes he made it more beautiful by setting in pieces of turquoise. Antelope wanted to be a silversmith but every

time he spoke of it to his father he replied, "Not yet, there is lots of time."

"Nothing interesting ever happens," grumbled Antelope to himself one morning, as he drove the flock from the pen, where they had spent the night. "Every morning I take out these sheep. All day I walk around with them. In the evening I drive them back into their pen. When Father was a boy, the Pawnees used to come to steal the sheep. Now the Pawnees stay at home and all the days are alike."

But one evening when he reached home, his father had good news for him.

"Tomorrow," Red Eagle said, "I am going to gather piñon nuts. Your mother thinks Little Hawk can take care of the flock for a few days. So I will take you with me."

Antelope was happy when he rolled himself into his sheepskin for the night. And Little Hawk, his brother, was happy, too. He liked to take care of the flock, and he was very happy he was old enough to be sent out with the animals.

Red Eagle and Antelope rode all the next morning, through the sand and sage bushes. The sun was very hot, but they were used to it. At noon they came to a ravine. There it was cool and shady and a little creek ran through it. Red Eagle said they would dismount and let the horses graze for a while.

Antelope turned his pony, Pinto, loose. He was so well trained, that he would come at his master's call. But Red Eagle's pony was new. He was not trained yet. So Red

Eagle tied a strip of leather, between one of the pony's
forefeet and one of his hind feet. In this way he could
graze around, but if he tried to run the hobble would trip
him.

Antelope and his father rested under the shade of a big tree. It was so still and cool that Antelope nearly went to sleep. But suddenly he heard his father whispering to him. "There is a Pawnee hidden behind that big rock," Red

Eagle whispered. "I just saw his head. Roll over under that thick bush beside you."

Antelope obeyed, and in an instant he was hidden by the lower branches of the bush. Then he saw Red Eagle spring up lightly and dart behind the tree. As he did so, a Pawnee came riding out from behind the big rock carrying a rifle. But just as he came into full sight of Antelope, he dropped down from his pony's back and disappeared from view. Antelope knew he was hanging down on the side of the pony. He knew, too, that while he stayed there, Red Eagle could not shoot him without first shooting the Pawnee's pony.

"He's going to steal our ponies," Antelope whispered excitedly.

Red Eagle did not answer but kept his rifle at his shoul-

der and pointed it at the Pawnee's pony, as it ran down the ravine.

When the Pawnee came to the hobbled pony, he reached down with his left hand to untie the hobble. This was what Red Eagle had been waiting for. As he saw the arm between the legs of the Pawnee's pony, he shot. With a yell of pain, the Pawnee shouted at his pony and rode like lightning out of the ravine.

Red Eagle and Antelope ran to their own ponies and mounted.

"Shall we follow the Pawnee?" Antelope asked.

Red Eagle shook his head. "I would not waste another shot on a thieving Pawnee," he said. "With my bullet in his left arm, it will be a long time before he will try to steal Navaho ponies again."

So they rode on, to the place where the piñon pines grew. There they filled their bags with the cones that hold the sweet piñon nuts. Then they turned their ponies' heads toward home.

They had been gone three days, when they rode up to the hogan at twilight. Antelope had had an adventure and had seen many strange and interesting things. But he was glad to smell the smoke of his mother's fire.

"And how has the new herder taken care of the flocks," Red Eagle asked after supper.

"Very well," White Cloud replied. "Little Hawk likes to take care of the animals. I have promised him that he may take them out every day now."

"That is good," said Red Eagle. "But what shall we do with Antelope? We can't have an idler about."

"I do not want to be an idler," Antelope said. "Tomorrow morning I shall come to you, for my first lesson in the art of the silversmith."

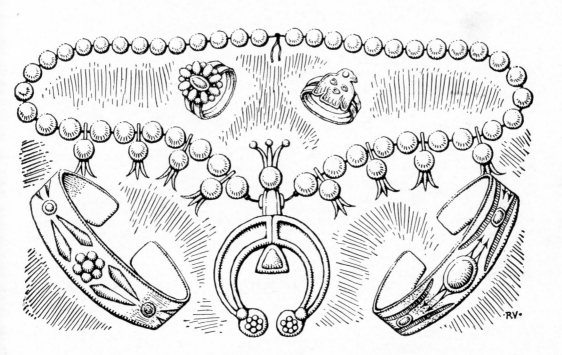

ROGER VERNAM

ANTELOPE

Antelope is this Indian's name
He rides and rides and when

He's tended all his father's flocks
He comes back home again.

How nice to have a pony
To feed lump sugar to.

What fun to ride across the plains
As little Indians do!

MORNING STAR—A LITTLE PUEBLO GIRL

Morning Star was a little Moki girl. The Moki Indians live in the Southwestern part of the United States, in big apartment houses called pueblos. "Pueblo" is the Spanish word for "village." The Spaniards were the first white people to visit this part of our country and they gave names to many of the things they found there.

The apartment house was built on the edge of a high cliff. The top of the cliff was flat. These flat-topped hills are called tablelands or mesas. "Mesa" is the Spanish word for "table."

The first floor had no windows and no doors in the wall. Nobody lived in it. It was used as a storeroom. The only light in it came from some small holes high up in the wall and from a trapdoor in the roof.

The second story, where Morning Star lived, was set back
as though it were the second step in a flight of stairs. To
get into her home, Morning Star climbed a ladder that
leaned against the roof of the first floor. Then she walked

across the roof to a door in the wall. To get into the store-room, she went through the trapdoor and down a ladder inside the room.

Pueblo children learn to climb almost as soon as they learn to walk. Even the dogs of the pueblos, go up and down the ladders.

At the bottom of the cliff Morning Star's father, Two Bears, had a garden. He grew cotton and squash and beans and corn of many colors. There were white ears and black ears. Others were yellow, or blue, or pink, or red, and some were speckled.

There was little rain in the Moki country, and the sun shone down very hot most of the year. So, long before Morning Star was born, the men of the pueblo had dug ditches from a river, to bring water to their gardens.

Morning Star liked to climb down the side of the mesa, when her father was working in his garden. Near the top, the cliff was almost as steep as the side of a house. The Indians who first chose the mesa for their home, had cut little steps or toeholds in the rock. As Morning Star went down, she put her toes and fingers into the little holes. It was almost like going down a ladder.

Morning Star spent most of her time on top of the mesa

with her mother, White Pigeon. She liked to watch her
mother make bread. When she was going to bake, White
Pigeon ground the colored corn between two stones. She
mixed this meal with water to make a thin batter. Then

she put into the fire a flat stone with a smooth top, like a pancake griddle.

When the stone was well heated White Pigeon poured a little of the batter on it and spread it very thin. It cooked

in just a second or two, and when she pulled it off, it looked like a round sheet of paper. While the second wafer was cooking, she folded the first over and over until it made a roll about the size of an ear of corn. This was the bread Morning Star ate almost every day. She liked it very much.

When White Pigeon had finished her housework, she made pottery from moist clay. She made all the dishes the family used. There were small bowls from which they ate. And there were larger bowls in which White Pigeon mixed bread or cooked meat or vegetables. The most interesting things she made were tall jars for holding or carrying water.

When she needed water, White Pigeon put one of these jars on top of her head. She walked across the roof and climbed down the ladder. Then she walked across the top of the mesa to the pool. Here she filled the jar and went back to her home. And all the time she was walking or climbing up or down the ladder, she did not even touch the jar with her hands.

Morning Star had often watched her mother making water jars. One day she decided she would make a little one for herself. She broke off a piece of the moist clay and rolled it into a ball. She flattened this out on the ground. Then she broke off another piece and rolled it into a long strip like a very large pencil.

She laid this strip around the edge of the flat piece and rubbed them together until they were smooth. Then she put another strip on top of the first. In this way she made her jar as tall as she wanted it. When it was finished, she buried it in the sand and built a little fire over it. The next day, when she dug it up, it was baked hard.

At first, when she put it on top of her head, she had to steady it with her hand. But soon she was able to balance it perfectly, without touching it. Soon she was able to go to the pool with White Pigeon every day and carry home fresh water for Two Bears to drink when he climbed up, hot and thirsty, from working in his garden.

MORNING STAR

Now would't it seem strange to you
To climb a ladder high

To get into your little house
Built way up near the sky?

But "Morning Star" is used to it
She's nimble as can be,—

And when she's up above the world
There's such a lot to see.

MICCO—A SEMINOLE INDIAN BOY

Micco was a Seminole Indian boy. He lived on an island in the Everglades of Florida. All around the island were miles and miles of swamps.

Micco never saw a mountain and would not have felt at home anywhere else but in the Everglades.

In some places the water was very shallow. These shallows were often filled with sawgrass. This is a tall, strong grass with sharp edges like the teeth of a saw. Where the sawgrass grew, it looked as though there was dry ground underneath. But Micco knew that if he stepped into it, he would sink into water and mud.

In other places the water formed deep lakes. In the deep

spots Micco's father could paddle his canoe. In the shallow
water, he pushed it ahead with a pole.

His canoe was a dugout. He made it from the trunk of
a cypress tree. The cypress is a tall tree, that grows on

the islands of the Everglades. The wood is very hard.

After he had cut down the tree trunk, Micco's father chopped a little hollow along the top. Then he built fires in the hollow. When the fires had burned out, he scraped away the charred wood. So he burned the hollow larger and larger, until his canoe was finished.

When Micco was only four, he began to help his father and mother with their work. He did not go to school, but his parents and grandparents taught him everything that a Seminole should know.

He learned to carry water from a spring to the wigwam where he lived. At first his mother gave him a little gourd to use as a pail. As he grew taller and stronger, she gave him larger ones, so he could carry more water at a time.

Micco's father was a great hunter. There was always plenty of meat in the wigwam. There were other good things to eat, also. Wild fruits and nuts grew on the islands of the Everglades. When Micco wanted an orange, his father picked one from a tree.

Micco's mother had a nice garden. In it she raised corn and sweet potatoes. She ground the corn into meal. From the meal she made bread. Back of the garden was a patch of sugar cane. His mother sometimes gave him a slice of sugar cane to suck. It tasted as good as your lollipops do.

Did you ever see a squash vine growing up a tree? There was a climbing squash in Micco's garden. It crept right up among the branches. The squashes looked as though they were growing on the tree, instead of on a vine.

When Micco's mother wanted to cook a squash, Micco's
father picked up his bow and an arrow. He shot the arrow
straight through the stem of one of the squashes. The
squash fell with a loud "Plop!" Then Micco ran to pick

it up. The squashes often broke when they touched the ground. Then Micco's mother did not even have to cut them open.

Micco's home was a wigwam. It looked a good deal like

the summer houses you sometimes see in gardens. It had a framework of poles. The floor was not placed on the ground. It was high enough for a dog or a baby to walk under and was made by fastening a floor of split poles to the framework and covering it with mats of woven reeds and grasses.

The sides of the wigwam were covered with deerskins to keep out the rain. During hot weather these were rolled up from the bottom like awnings. The roof was made of leaves which were tied to the framework and held fast at the top by heavy poles. They were very large leaves from the palmetto tree. Palm leaf fans are made from these leaves. They made a cool roof for the wigwam. The hot rays of the sun could not get through them. The heavy

rains ran right off this roof, too. So Micco's home was
cool and dry, no matter how hot or how wet the weather
might be.

All over the island tall trees grew. Some of them had
veils of gray moss hanging from the branches. These were
live oaks. When Micco climbed into a live oak tree, he was
hidden by the moss from anyone who was standing on the
ground.

The Everglades were full of interesting things. Some of
them were lovely to see. Some of them were dangerous.

His father showed him alligators and water snakes
when they were going through the swamps in their dugout canoe.

The alligators looked like rough logs lying on the water.

But when they opened their great jaws, Micco could see
rows of strong, sharp teeth.   He knew he must learn to
defend himself against alligators, when he was old enough
to be a hunter.

There were many wonderful things to see, in this Everglade country. Beautiful birds of all colors. Micco liked to watch the white herons scooping up little fish in their big bills. He knew they were getting food for the hungry little herons, which were waiting in mud nests in the trees. The loveliest birds of all were the pink flamingoes, which stood on one leg in the swamps.

Often Micco heard wild turkeys "gobbling" in the trees. He learned to "gobble" too. Somtimes the turkeys thought he was another turkey, calling to them. Then they called back to him.

Micco was never lonely, even when he went into the woods alone. He liked to watch the birds and animals and insects. Sometimes he made friends with them. He knew he must learn all about these woodland creatures, to become a good hunter in the Seminole tribe.

MICCO

"What pretty birds" young Micco thinks
As he sees them flying high.

Their feathers are a dainty pink
Against the blue, blue sky.

"I'd like to jump upon one's back
And float right thru the air

I know it would be lots of fun
But—guess I wouldn't dare."

WATLALA—AN INDIAN BOY OF THE NORTHWEST

Watlala was a little Indian boy. He belonged to the Killamook tribe. His home was on the shore of the Pacific Ocean.

A large river ran down from the Cascade Mountains into the Ocean and thick forests grew close to Watlala's home. Berries and wild turnips grew in the forest and there were bears and deer and many other wild animals. But the Killamook Indians liked fish better than any other food.

In order to catch fish in the Ocean and rivers, the Killa-mooks needed canoes. The men made them out of cedar trees. Some of them were so big, that thirty or forty men could travel in one canoe.

They painted the insides of the canoes red. On the outside they carved animals and birds and fish. The Killa-
mooks had no steel tools. So they had to do their carving
with sharpened stones or bits of obsidian. Obsidian is a
hard dark-colored glass, that is found in places where there
are volcanoes. It is hard to carve with stone or obsidian
tools, but the Indians were patient workers and carved almost everything they used.

They made carved wooden dishes, and in front of every
house, they set up a totem pole with animals and birds and
fish carved on it. The animal or bird or fish at the top of
the pole, was the totem of the family that lived in the house.

This totem was always put on the bow of their canoe. The Indians believed that their totems would act as guardian spirits, to help and protect them. Watlala's family had the bear as their totem, so on top of the pole before his home, the figure of a bear was carved.

The house in which Watlala lived was a large one. Many other families lived in it. They were all cousins, aunts or uncles, nephews or nieces, to one another. They all had the bear as their totem.

Watlala's father and the other men of the village, spent most of their time catching fish. The greatest fishing time was when the salmon swam up the river to lay their eggs.

When Watlala was six years old, he and his mother went up the river to watch his father spear salmon. They camped on the bank of the big river near a little waterfall.

When the salmon came to the fall, Watlala thought they would have to turn around and swim back. But instead of being discouraged, the salmon leaped high into the air to clear the waterfall. After many attempts most of them

were able to jump above the waterfall and go up the river. Every once in a while, one flopped right out onto the bank, where Watlala's mother was waiting for it.

As fast as the salmon were caught they were split and dried in the hot sun or in the smoke from fires. Then they were carefully packed away to be used for food in the winter.

The greatest excitement of all was when a whale was seen in the Ocean near Watlala's home. Then the men set off in their big carved canoes. They took harpoons and long ropes to catch the whale.

Watlala went down to the beach to watch the men getting ready for the whale hunt. He was too young to go with them, but he helped to carry the harpoons and ropes to the canoes.

After the big canoes had disappeared, Watlala dug clams on the beach. He put them into a basket. When he had all he could carry, he hung the basket on his back and took them home.

His mother made a stew of some of the clams for dinner. She strung the rest on a string made of twisted grasses and hung them over the fire to dry.

When the whalers came paddling back, towing an immense whale, there was a great feast in the village. Everyone knew that there would be plenty of meat for a long time. Best of all, there would be lots of blubber oil, which

Watlala and his friends liked as much as we like butter and they dipped into it nearly everything they ate.

Most of the men had false faces carved from wood, which they put on for the dancing after the feast. Watlala had one that his father had made him. It had eyes that would roll around in their sockets and a mouth that would open and shut when he pulled little strings that hung down inside.

Watlala put on his false face and danced around with the men, until he was so tired he could hardly stand. Then he went home and put the false face carefully away. He rolled himself up in his blankets and went to sleep. It was a very happy night for him, because he dreamed that he was eating all the dried clams he wanted, with plenty of blubber oil to dip them in.

WATLALA

Watlala is this Indian boy
He lives in the far Northwest;

To watch his father salmon fish
Is what he likes the best.

The clams he carries on his back
His mother puts in stew

He thinks it's fun to dig for them
I guess we'd like it too.

NIGALEK—A LITTLE ESKIMO BOY

Nigalek was a little Eskimo boy. He lived near the North Pole, where it is very cold most of the time. But he did not mind the cold. His mother, Igliuk, made lots of warm clothes for him, out of furs his father brought home from hunting.

The house in which Nigalek lived all winter, looked like a giant's bowl turned upside down. It is called an igloo. His father Kipmak, built it of blocks of frozen snow. To get into or out of the igloo Nigalek had to crawl through a snow tunnel.

In the igloo there was a big flat dish of stone. This was the stove. In it Igliuk burned whale oil. It gave the only heat in the igloo, and over it all their food was cooked.

Meat and fish were the only food the Eskimos had all winter. Even in summer they had very little else. Once some white men came to Nigalek's home. They gave him some little pink things that they called gumdrops. Nigalek thought he had never tasted anything so good before. It was the first time he had eaten candy.

He used to wish that more white men would come and bring him gumdrops. His father laughed. He promised to bring some the next time he went to the white trader with his furs. But the trader was many days' journey away.

One day Kipmak came home with good news. A ship was frozen in the ice. One of the neighbors had been there. The white men on board were buying furs and paying for

them with rifles and knives and other things that the Eskimos needed.

"Get ready," Kipmak said to Igliuk. "It is only two days' journey. I will take you and Nigalek."

Nigalek was very happy and excited. He ran around the igloo helping his mother pack for the journey. His father loaded a great pile of furs on his sledge. Then he harnessed up his eight dogs.

Igliuk came out with some bundles. Nigalek knew they contained meat for their meals on the journey and some blubber to make a fire when they camped at night. She tied the bundles to one side of the sledge. Kipmak tied his rifle and a little tent of skin to the other side.

He lifted Nigalek up and set him on top of the pile of
skins. Then he snapped his long whip and shouted to the
dogs. Off they started, and Nigalek felt his sledge begin
to move under him.

Kipmak did not get on the sledge. He ran along behind it on one side, and Igliuk ran on the other side. When Nigalek saw that he wanted to get down and run too. But his mother told him to stay on the sledge.

"Your legs are not long enough to keep up with us," she said. "And your weight does not add much to the load the dogs have to pull."

Nigalek was glad. It was fun riding on top of the pile of furs, and he liked to watch the dogs running ahead over the hard snow.

After they had been going for several hours, they came to the top of a steep hill. Nigalek liked going down hills. The sledge slipped along so fast that his father and mother stood on the back, to keep it from running into the dogs. But just as they reached the top of this hill, Kipmak gave a shout and stopped the dogs.

"Nanook," he shouted.

Nigalek knew that Nanook was a polar bear. And, there, sure enough, right in their path at the bottom of the hill, a great white beast was standing. He looked up with wicked little eyes. Then he began to run up the hill.

Nigalek was frightened. He knew that Nanook was very fierce and strong. But Kipmak pulled his rifle from the sledge and, taking careful aim, shot. Nanook fell over dead and rolled to the bottom of the hill.

There was great excitement for the rest of the day. Kipmak skinned the bear and cut up the meat. The dogs howled and jumped around. They knew there would be fresh meat for their supper, instead of dried fish.

"We must hide the meat near here," said Igliuk. "When we come back from the trader's our sledge will be much lighter. Then we will be able to take the meat home with us."

"But we will have a steak for supper tonight, won't we?" asked Nigalek.

"Oh, yes," Igliuk promised.

Kipmak was looking at the great bearskin.

"It is a very fine pelt," he said. "Since this is Nigalek's first visit to a trader's, I will let him have it to sell."

"That will be nice," agreed Igliuk. "And what will you ask the trader to give you for the bearskin, my son?"

Nigalek thought for a moment. "I want a hunting knife and gumdrops," he shouted. "Many, many gumdrops."

NIGALEK

Nigalek's home is made of ice
Like a bowl turned upside down.

It stands alone away up North
(There isn't any town.)

His fur-lined suit is just the thing
To protect him from the snow.

His mother made it for him and
It keeps him warm you know.